بِسْمِ اللَّهِ الرَّحْمَٰنِ الرَّحِيمِ

اَللّٰهُمَّ صَلِّ عَلٰى سَيِّدِنَا مُحَمَّدٍ وَّ سَيِّدِنَا آدَمَ وَ سَيِّدِنَا نُوْحٍ وَّ سَيِّدِنَا إِبْرَاهِيمَ وَ سَيِّدِنَا مُوْسٰى وَ سَيِّدِنَا عِيْسٰى وَ مَا بَيْنَهُمْ مِنَ النَّبِيِّيْنَ وَ الْمُرْسَلِيْنَ صَلَوَاتُ اللّٰهِ وَ سَلَامُهُ عَلَيْهِمْ أَجْمَعِيْنَ

Allah's name I begin with, the Most Kind, the Most Merciful.

O Allah, bless our master Muhammad, and our master Adam, and our master Noah, and our master Abraham, and our master Moses, and our master Jesus and all the Prophets and Messengers between them; the blessings and peace of Allah be upon all of them.

PROPHETS in The Qur'an
ACTIVITY TIMELINE

M N Sialvi & H B Sahibzada

STI Publishing
info@stipublishing.co.uk
www.stipublishing.co.uk | www.dhikarville.co.uk

Prophets in The Qur'an © 2017 STI Publishing

Printed by Imak Ofset Turkey

ISBN 978 1 9079330 9 7

Publishing

Contents

How To Use This Book

This book is designed to be used as a timeline. No doubt, many teachers and parents will tailor the use of the book to suit their style and setting, and that's great. Here are some ideas to get you started. Each story consists of an activity sheet to colour, some background information and some lessons to be learned. We have tried to keep the information as concise and straightforward as possible. This is so that the book can be used by all ages. For very small children, the teacher should read out the information and explain it in terms that engage their imagination. Older children can be encouraged to read the background information on their own or aloud in the classroom, whilst advanced students may be given supplementary information by the teacher to fill in the details of the stories. The greyed out areas on some activity sheets are for stickers which can be found at the back of the book.

These stories are about the noble prophets mentioned by name in the Blessed Qur'an. Where possible, students should be given a lesson or moral to learn from each story, so that the blessings of the Noble Qur'an can be experienced fully.

Respect lies at the heart of the creed of the *Ahl as-Sunna*, it underpins all our beliefs and practices. We have tried our best to get this across so students can learn to honour the noble messengers in their hearts and speak of them with *adab*.

The activity pages are designed to be removed from the book and displayed in a line on the wall to form a timeline. In a classroom setting, it may not be possible to display every student's work so one idea is to ask the students to compete in producing the best work and then select a winner to take the place on the wall. The rest can leave their activity pages inside their books or make their own timeline at home.

Although the background information is designed to stay in the book so as to form a reference point to return to, it is also possible to display the background text with each activity sheet below the timeline.

We pray that Allah Almighty makes this book useful for you and brings fun and benefit to your students, *ameen*.

M N Sialvi & H B Sahibzada

Prophet Adam
& Lady Hawwa

عليهما السلام

1

Prophet Adam and Lady Hawwa عليهما السلام

- Prophet Adam عليه السلام was the first human to be created.
- Allah ﷻ taught him the names and uses of all things.
- He then commanded all the angels to bow in front of Prophet Adam عليه السلام to show him respect because he had all this knowledge. All the angels obeyed Allah ﷻ but Iblees (the Shaytan) did not obey.
- Prophet Adam's wife, Lady Hawwa, was created to be his companion and life partner so he would not be lonely.
- They were both allowed to live in Jannah but Allah ﷻ told them not to go near one tree.
- The wicked Shaytan tricked them into going near the tree by saying to them that if they ate the fruit of this tree they would live in Jannah forever. They forgot about Allah's command and ate the fruit of the tree.
- Prophet Adam and Lady Hawwa عليهما السلام were then sent to the Earth to live here for a fixed time.
- They were very sorry for eating from the forbidden tree so Allah ﷻ forgave them.
- Our life in this world is a test to see if we obey Allah ﷻ or not. If we do good things and stay away from bad deeds then Allah ﷻ will be pleased with us and let us go to Jannah when we die. Whoever goes to Jannah will live happily there forever.

Lessons

- Prophet Adam ﷺ is Ab al-Bashar (the father of humanity) so all people are brothers and sisters. No one is superior due to their lineage, colour or race.
- Knowledge and those who bear it should be respected.
- It is an example of Allah Almighty's infinite mercy that he gave us family so we are not lonely in the world. We should keep the ties of kinship and not cut off from family members.
- Obeying Allah ﷻ is an angelic trait and disobeying Allah ﷻ is the way of Satan.
- Forgetting is part of the human condition and Allah ﷻ will not hold us to account for things outside our control.
- When we make a mistake we should repent for it straight away and say sorry if our mistake affects others too. Being truly sorry means not making the same mistake again.
- We should try to be good in this life so we can return to Jannah which is the eternal home that Allah ﷻ has made for us.

Prophet Idrees

عليه السلام

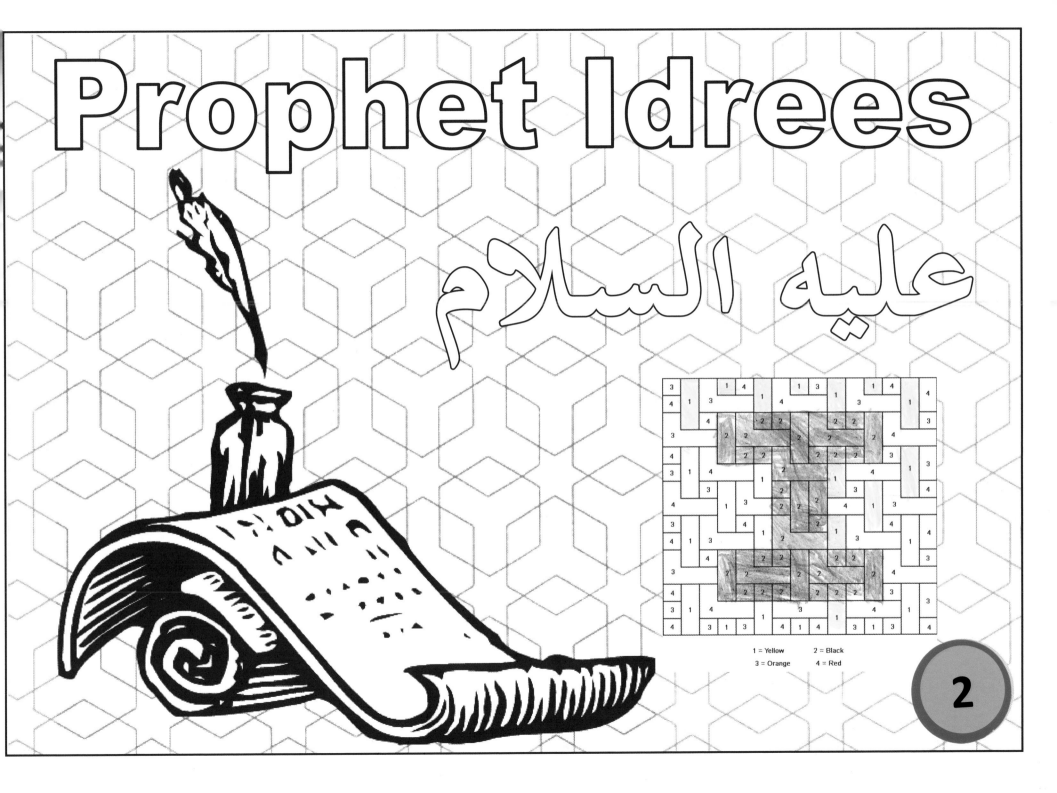

1 = Yellow   2 = Black

3 = Orange   4 = Red

2

Prophet Idrees عليه السلام

- Prophet Idrees عليه السلام was the next prophet after Prophet Adam عليه السلام.
- He was sent by Allah ﷻ because the people forgot the teachings of Prophet Adam عليه السلام about obeying and worshipping Allah ﷻ and instead the Shaytan led them towards worshipping idols.
- Prophet Idrees عليه السلام taught them to come back to the path of Allah ﷻ which is the true path.
- It is said that Prophet Idrees عليه السلام was the first person to be given the knowledge of writing and the knowledge of numbers.
- He is known as Enoch in the Torah and Bible.
- He is mentioned twice in the Holy Qur'an.

Lessons

- Each prophet was sent when the teachings of the previous prophet were forgotten, lost or changed in order to guide people back to the straight path (after Prophet Muhammad ﷺ, the last prophet, the righteous scholars continue this task).

- Learning to read and write is an important skill. Writing is a tool to capture knowledge so it is retained for the benefit of others. Much of our knowledge of history only exists because people wrote things down.

- The knowledge of maths is very important too. We all use one branch of maths or another every day. Algorithms, for example, make most of our technology possible.

Prophet Nuh عليه السلام and the flood

3

Prophet Nuh عليه السلام

- After Prophet Idrees عليه السلام passed away, slowly people forgot his teachings and so Allah ﷻ sent Prophet Nuh عليه السلام to call people back to the true path.

- Prophet Nuh عليه السلام invited people to the truth for 950 years.

- In all this time, only a few people, about 70 altogether, became his true followers. Everyone else called him a liar and the rich people said that he only wanted people to follow him so he could become rich and powerful, but this was not true.

- In the end Allah ﷻ instructed him to build an ark - a huge boat. While he worked at building the Ark, the people made fun of him for building a boat in the middle of a desert. They thought he was mad, but he was following Allah's orders.

- When the Ark was finished, Allah ﷻ told Prophet Nuh عليه السلام to take his followers and pairs of animals on board because there would be a huge flood.

- Everyone who refused to board the Ark drowned in the flood including one of Prophet Nuh's sons who wanted to be with his friends rather than on the Ark.

- The Ark rested on Mount Judi after 40 days when the rain finally stopped and the water began to go down.

- Allah Almighty continued the human race through the survivors on the Ark.

Lessons

- The messengers are all truthful and they convey the message of Allah ﷻ with honesty so we should listen to them and obey them.
- If people disobey Allah ﷻ and his messengers then Allah Almighty's punishment comes to them.
- Allah ﷻ is powerful over everything. He can create a sea in a desert or dry up a sea into a desert without any difficulty whatsoever.
- Allah ﷻ can wipe out a family, a tribe, a nation or all of humanity in one cataclysmic event if He wills it.
- It is a person's deeds which matter in the end, not their family background. Prophet Nuh's son drowned in the flood despite being from a noble family because he chose the wrong company.

Prophet Hud

عليه السلام

and the People of Ad

IRAM: THE CITY OF COLUMNS

4

Prophet Hud عليه السلام

- Prophet Hud عليه السلام was sent to the people of Ad.
- The people of Ad were a very advanced civilisation who had built a city of beautiful grand buildings called Iram - the city of columns. This city is mentioned in the Blessed Qur'an.
- The nation of Ad were wealthy and powerful, but also arrogant and unjust.
- A mighty wind was sent upon them when they disobeyed Prophet Hud عليه السلام and refused to be fair and faithful.
- The wind which came as their punishment howled and raged for seven nights and eight long days.
- The powerful wind destroyed everything in their grand city leaving behind only ruins and rubble.

Lessons

- Arrogance and pride are not good qualities; they lead to downfall.
- Being gifted should lead to humility and gratefulness, not arrogance and pride.
- Allah Almighty showed the People of Ad that the tall buildings with beautiful columns they made were no match for the wind sent by Allah ﷻ.
- Allah ﷻ can grant us benefit from the wind which blows rain clouds to water crops but the same wind can be turned to a deadly force of destruction - this shows Allah Almighty's limitless power.
- If we live in a cosmopolitan world of tall skyscrapers we shouldn't get too comfortable with that. The tall buildings should remind us of the People of Ad and keep us humble.

Prophet Salih

عليه السلام

and the people of Thamud

City of Petra, Jordan.

5

Prophet Salih عليه السلام

- Prophet Salih ﷺ was sent to the people of Thamud who were great architects and builders, but they had become arrogant.
- The leaders of Thamud plotted to kill Prophet Salih ﷺ, but they failed to do that.
- They demanded a miracle as a sign from Allah ﷻ that Prophet Salih ﷺ was calling them to the truth.
- They asked for a huge rock to split open and for a she-camel to come out of the rock. The she-camel was not like normal camels, it was huge and ate and drank lots but it gave enough milk for all the people of Thamud.
- Allah ﷻ showed them this great miracle through Prophet Salih ﷺ but warned them not to harm the she-camel.
- The people of Thamud killed the she-camel by cutting her hamstrings.
- A mighty bolt of lightning came as their punishment leaving them lifeless and helpless, face-down in their ruins.

Lessons

- The lessons regarding arrogance and pride from the People of Ad also apply here to the story of the People of Thamud.

- It is not wise to make demands which you cannot respect if they are granted.

- The she-camel from the story of Prophet Salih ﷺ is called *"naaqatullah"* in the Blessed Qur'an - it means the she-camel of Allah. Although everything belongs to Allah, this was a special creature which was a sign of Allah ﷻ, so it is given this honorary name.

- The story teaches us to honour and respect the signs of Allah Almighty.

Prophet Lut

عليه السلام

and his guests

6

Prophet Lut عليه السلام

- Prophet Lut عليه السلام was sent to the people of Sodom and Gomorrah.
- They rejected the message of Prophet Lut عليه السلام and disobeyed Allah عز وجل.
- Allah عز وجل sent some Angels in the form of men to warn Prophet Lut عليه السلام about the punishment that would be sent upon his people because of their sins.
- Prophet Lut's wife betrayed them by telling the people about the secret guests of Prophet Lut عليه السلام.
- When the people found out about the special guests they tried to break down the door so that they could take the guests away and harm them.
- Their punishment came in the form of a storm of burning rocks which rained down upon the people (possibly a volcanic eruption).
- Allah عز وجل saved Prophet Lut عليه السلام and his followers, but the rest of the people, including his wife, all died in the punishment.

Lessons

- If you are entrusted to keep a secret you should not betray the trust.
- You should honour your guests by treating them with kindness and generosity so that they feel at home.
- Prophet Lut's wife betrayed his trust and joined the idol worshippers so Allah ﷻ punished her alongside them and they all perished. Being with people who do wrong things leads to a person's destruction.
- The people that Prophet Lut عليه السلام was sent to wanted to follow their own desires. We learn from their destruction that humans can desire wrong things and this is why Allah ﷻ sent divine revelation to guide us.

Prophet Ibrahim

صحف ابراهيم

The Scrolls
of Abraham

عليه السلام

and the tests

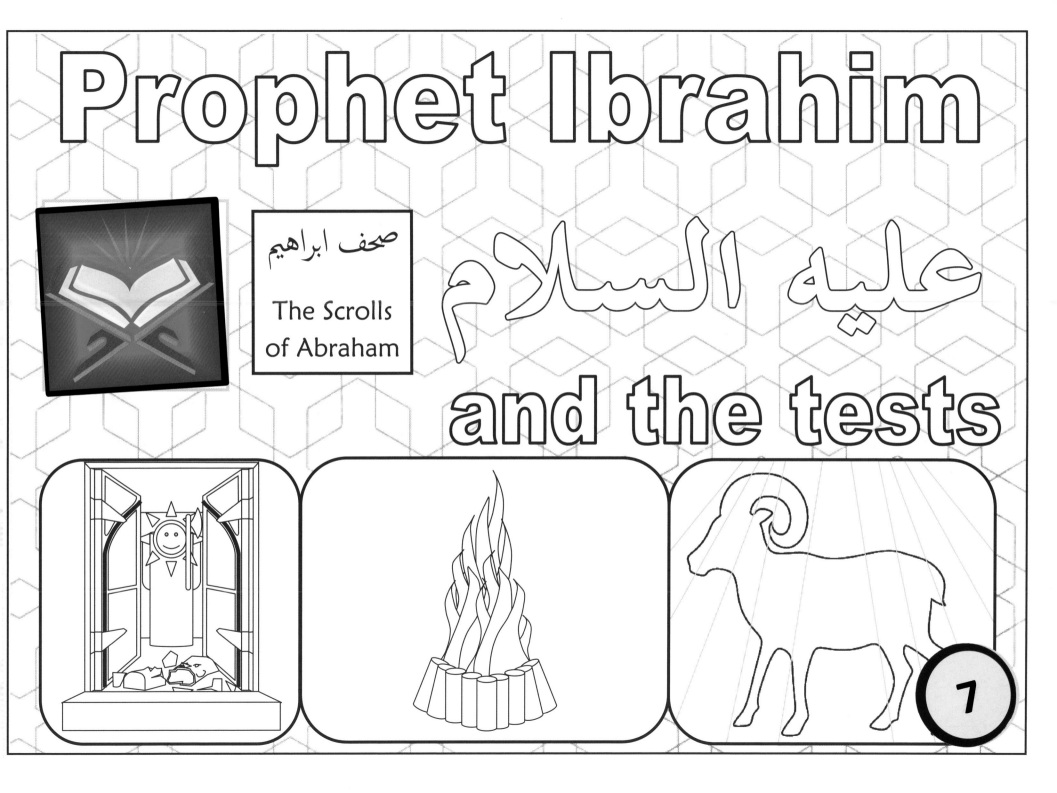

7

Prophet Ibrahim عليه السلام

- When Prophet Ibrahim عليه السلام was just a boy, he saw people worshipping idols - the same idols they had carved with their own hands. This seemed very strange to him so he rejected the worship of idols. This was a test of his faith.

- It made him so upset that, while everybody was at the carnival, he took an axe and smashed all the idols in the temple except the biggest one. He then left the axe hanging around the neck of the biggest idol.

- When the people saw this they suspected Prophet Ibrahim عليه السلام because he rejected the idols. He said to them, "Why don't you ask the biggest one?" This angered the people and they took him to the king Nimrod.

- Nimrod had a huge fire built to burn Prophet Ibrahim عليه السلام. The fire was so big that it was impossible to get near it without burning from the heat. Even birds couldn't fly over it! The king's soldiers placed Prophet Ibrahim عليه السلام into a catapult and shot him towards the fire from a distance. This was a test of his Trust in Allah تعالى.

- Allah تعالى commanded the fire to be cool for His friend, Prophet Ibrahim عليه السلام, so he was unharmed.

- When he was an old man Allah تعالى gave him a son after years and years of du'as but then ordered him to sacrifice his son Prophet Ismail عليه السلام. This was a test of his patience and his love and obedience towards Allah تعالى. Both, father and son, passed the test and a ram from heaven was sacrificed in place of Prophet Ismail عليه السلام. This example is followed by millions of people every year on Eid al-Adha.

Prophet Ibrahim عليه السلام

- Prophet Ibrahim ﷺ and Prophet Ismail ﷺ built the Ka'ba together. There is still a stone with Prophet Ibrahim's footprint near the Ka'ba to this day called Maqam Ibrahim.
- His title is Khalilullah - the close friend of Allah.
- He was given scripture called the scrolls of Abraham.
- He is revered by the three major world religions: Judaism, Christianity and Islam.

Lessons

- Sometimes children can guide elders when Allah ﷻ wants to guide his people.
- You should not be afraid to stand up for what is right even if you are small.
- Allah ﷻ does not forsake his servants when they place their trust in Him.
- Everything in creation serves those who serve Allah ﷻ sincerely.
- Allah Almighty tests us all; the greater the person, the greater the test.
- Those who pass the test and please Allah ﷻ live on forever in people's memories and actions.
- Life is a series of tests to see who follows their own wishes and who follows Allah Almighty's commands.

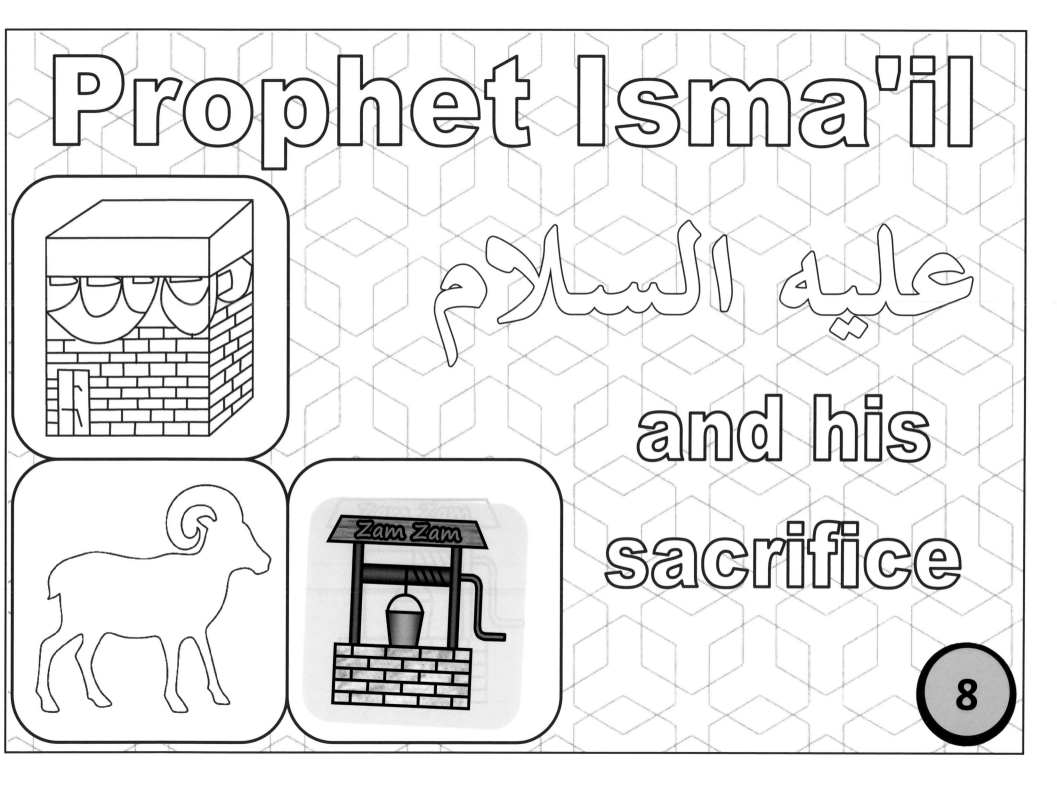

Prophet Isma'il

عليه السلام

and his sacrifice

8

Prophet Ismail عليه السلام

- Prophet Ismail عليه السلام was the first son of Prophet Ibrahim عليه السلام born to Lady Hajra.
- He was left with his mother in the desert valley of Bakka, alone hungry and thirsty.
- The miracle of Zamzam water was due to his hunger and thirst.
- He showed exceptional faith, patience and steadfastness when his father was going to sacrifice him.
- He helped his father Prophet Ibrahim عليه السلام to build the Holy Ka'ba.

Lessons

- Prophet Ismail's trust and respect for his father, Prophet Ibrahim عليه السلام, is an example for children to honour and respect their parents. Prophet Muhammad ﷺ said that you should obey your parents in everything as long as it does not mean disobeying Allah ﷻ.

- Prophet Ismail عليه السلام helped Prophet Ibrahim عليه السلام to rebuild the Holy Ka'ba - this teaches us to help our parents in their jobs and tasks, especially those which are done for the sake of Allah ﷻ.

- Prophet Ismail عليه السلام showed an incredible level of patience and steadfastness when Prophet Ibrahim عليه السلام told him about his dream in which he saw himself sacrificing Prophet Ismail عليه السلام for the sake of Allah ﷻ. He replied, "My dear father, do what you have been commanded [by Allah]. God willing, you will find that I am from those who are steadfast."

Prophet Ishaq

عليه السلام

the promised baby of Lady Sara

9

Prophet Ishaq عليه السلام

- Prophet Ishaq ﷺ was the second son of Prophet Ibrahim ﷺ born to Lady Sara when she was very old and well past the normal age of having children.
- The good news of his birth was given to Prophet Ibrahim ﷺ by the angels on their way to destroy the people of Prophet Lut ﷺ.
- His birth brought great joy to his very old parents.
- Prophet Ishaq ﷺ led a beautiful life; he is described in the Qur'an as someone who was righteous, purified, who established salah, gave in charity and did good deeds. He was blessed with the reward that all major prophets after him except Prophet Muhammad ﷺ were from his offspring.

Lessons

- A lesson from Prophet Ishaq's story is that if you live a life of dedication to God, then one of the rewards may be good, pious offspring.

Prophet Ya'qub

عليه السلام

ISRAEL
father of
12 sons

اسرآئيل
Israel

يوسف
Joseph

رؤبين
Reuben

شمعون
Simeon

بنيامين
Benjamin

Rachel

روي
Levi

Leah

Dan
دان

Judah

Bilha
بلها

Naphtali
نفتالي

Issachar

Zilpa
زلفا

Zebulon

Asher

Gad
جاد

10

Prophet Ya'qub عليه السلام

- Prophet Ya'qub عليه السلام is also known as Israel. He was Prophet Ishaq's son and Prophet Ibrahim's grandson.
- Prophet Ya'qub عليه السلام had twelve sons whose descendants became the twelve tribes of *Bani Israeel* (The Israelites)
- Prophet Ya'qub عليه السلام loved his son Yusuf more than the others because he had been chosen by Almighty Allah to be a Prophet and great leader.
- Prophet Yusuf عليه السلام and his brother *Binyamin* (Benjamin) were born to Prophet Ya'qub's wife called *Raheel* (Rachel).
- From his other wife Leah they were blessed with six sons; Reuben, Simeon, Levi, Judah, Issacher and Zebulon.
- Gad and Asher were born to the handmaiden of Leah called Zilpa.
- Bilha, the handmaiden of Rachel gave birth to two sons; Dan and Napthali.

Lessons

- Prophet Ya'qub ﷺ understood his sons' personalities so he gave them all advice according to that. The lesson here is for someone in a position of authority to be sincere in advising others and it is wise to give counsel tailored to the one receiving it.

- Prophet Yaq'ub ﷺ was extremely patient when his sons lied to him about the wolf killing Prophet Yusuf ﷺ and their scheming, even though Allah Almighty had blessed him with knowledge and insight, he waited patiently as Allah Almighty's plan unfolded. Sometimes elders watch youngsters making mistakes even though they can see the outcome before it happens due to their life experience but occasionally they know that the youngsters need to make the mistake in order to learn from it.

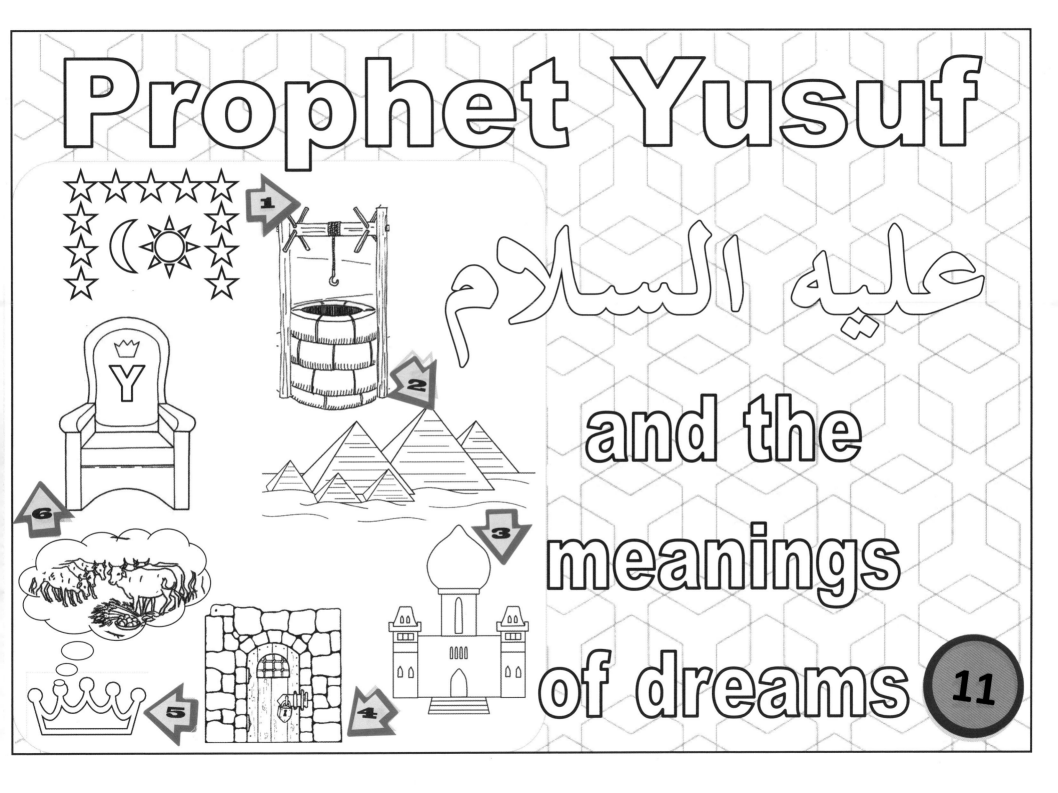

Prophet Yusuf عليه السلام

- Prophet Yusuf عليه السلام had a dream when he was just a young boy. He saw that the sun, moon and eleven stars were bowing to him.
- His father knew that this dream meant great things were in store for his favourite son. He advised him to keep the dream a secret from his brothers because they would be jealous.
- The brothers were indeed jealous of their father's love for Prophet Yusuf عليه السلام and threw him into a well.
- From the well he was captured by travellers and sold as a slave in Egypt where he ended up in the ownership of an important leader of the country who had no children of his own.
- The leader's wife had him thrown into prison based on false accusations when she told him to do something wrong but he refused.
- While he was in prison the king had a dream. He saw seven thin cows who ate seven fat cows and he saw seven withered, dry wheat stalks and seven green, fresh wheat stalks. No one could interpret this dream except Prophet Yusuf عليه السلام because Allah ﷻ gave him special knowledge of interpreting dreams.
- He interpreted the dream to mean that there would be seven years of good harvest followed by seven years of severe drought. He was released from prison when the king realised the accusations against him were false and appointed him as a governor.
- All of Prophet Yusuf's family came from Canaan to live in Egypt where they bowed down to him out of respect; and so the dream he had seen as a child came true.

Lessons

- Prophet Yusuf ﷺ took advice from his father regarding his dream as a boy, youngsters should seek advice from those with more experience.

- Prophet Yusuf ﷺ had the opportunity to take advantage of the situation when the leader's wife was plotting to betray her husband and wanted Prophet Yusuf ﷺ to be involved in the betrayal, but he refused because he knew Allah ﷻ is aware of her plan. He said "I would rather go to prison than to be involved in your plan." The lesson is to always act with integrity. Even when an opportunity arises to take advantage of a situation and get away with it; know that Allah ﷻ is watching.

- Even in prison Prophet Yusuf ﷺ continued to tell the inmates about monotheism and helped them with his gift of interpreting dreams. There are several lessons here; firstly, if you have a duty to fulfil, nothing should deter you from doing that (even being in prison); secondly, no matter how dire your situation may seem, try to find the positive in it and know that it may well prove to be the doorway to immense goodness; thirdly, if Allah Almighty has given you a gift, use it for the service and benefit of others because Allah ﷻ loves those who help His creation.

- Prophet Yusuf ﷺ sent his shirt to be placed on Prophet Ya'qub's face to restore his sight when he learned of his blindness. Allah ﷻ places blessings in things that come into contact with his chosen slaves.

- One of the most profound lessons to be learned from this story is the lesson of forgiveness. In the end, Prophet Yusuf ﷺ forgave his brothers for the terrible way in which they had treated him. He showed them kindness and generosity instead.

Prophet Ayyub

عليه السلام

and his patience during illness

12

Prophet Ayyub عليه السلام

- Allah ﷻ tested Prophet Ayyub عليه السلام by taking away his wealth, health and family.
- His body was covered in sores. People stayed away from him. Even poor beggars did not go near him and his family left him too.
- Prophet Ayyub عليه السلام was very patient. He had faith and trust in Allah ﷻ. He did not complain to anyone about his condition but instead he turned to Allah ﷻ for help.
- Allah Almighty told him to strike the ground with his foot. When he did this, a spring of water welled up from the ground. When he washed his body with the water, all his sores were healed. Allah ﷻ gave him his wealth and family back too.
- Allah ﷻ also rewarded Prophet Ayyub's patience by giving him a son who was a prophet: Prophet Dhul Kifl عليه السلام.

Lessons

- Prophet Ayyub's story teaches us that sometimes hardship and misfortune come to people not because of their wrong actions, but as a test from Allah ﷻ.
- Allah ﷻ does not waste our efforts for his sake, and rewards patience especially handsomely.
- We should turn to Allah ﷻ when we are afflicted with difficulty and ask him to ease the difficulty. This does not mean that we forget to pray to Allah ﷻ when things are going well, we should strive to remember Allah in sad and happy times. Prophet Muhammad ﷺ said, "The situation of the believer is a strange one, when he is happy he praises and thanks Allah ﷻ and is rewarded for that; when he is in difficulty he praises Allah ﷻ and shows patience and is rewarded for that!" [Al-Bayhaqi]

Prophet Dhul Kifl

عليه السلام

the son of

Prophet Ayyub

عليه السلام

IRAQ

It is said that the grave of Prophet Dhul Kifl عليه السلام is in a place called Kefil in Iraq.

13

Prophet Dhul Kifl عليه السلام

- Prophet Dhul Kifl عليه السلام was the son of Prophet Ayyub عليه السلام.
- He is mentioned twice by name in the Blessed Qur'an.
- Prophet Dhul Kifl عليه السلام is mentioned very briefly in the Blessed Qur'an. He is described as "steadfast" and "righteous."
- It is said that he is buried in the town of Kefil in present day Iraq and that this is where he gets his name from.
- Prophet Dhul Kifl عليه السلام is said to be the man who is known by the Jews and Christians as the Prophet Ezekiel.

Lessons

- We should strive to life our lives in a good manner so that if someone was to sum up our lives in a word, the word would be a good and profound one.

Prophet Shoaib عليه السلام

- Prophet Shoaib عليه السلام was sent to the people of Madyan, a nomadic tribe of north-western Arabia.
- Madyan was an elder of the tribe and the tribe was named after him.
- The people of Madyan had become idol worshippers and were not honest in their trade dealings. They tricked and short-changed other people who they traded with.
- Prophet Shoaib عليه السلام told his people to worship only Allah سبحانه وتعالى and to be honest in their dealings with other people. Most of them rejected his message and refused to worship Allah سبحانه وتعالى so they were destroyed by a punishment.
- The punishment of Allah Almighty came in the form of a huge blast which destroyed everyone but Allah سبحانه وتعالى saved Prophet Shoaib عليه السلام and his followers.
- Prophet Shoaib عليه السلام was the father-in-law of Prophet Musa عليه السلام.

Lessons

- Honesty in trade dealings is one of the messages from the story of Prophet Shoaib ﷺ. Our faith teaches us to be absolutely upright and honest, never to cheat or short-change anyone. One of the secrets behind the rapid spread of Islam in the early days was the ethical and principled dealings of Muslim traders. When they travelled along the trade routes they left an impression wherever they went and a trail of converts to the faith.

Prophet Musa

عليه السلام

& Pharaoh

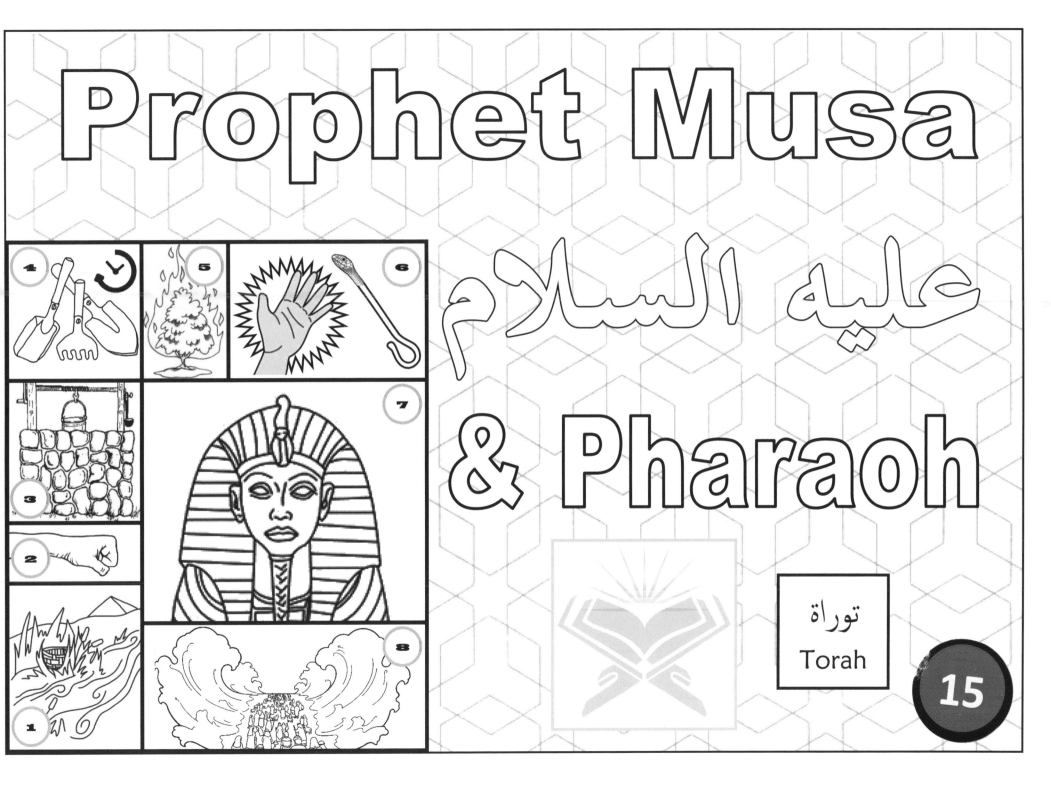

توراة
Torah

15

Prophet Musa عليه السلام

- Prophet Musa عليه السلام was born amongst the Children of Israel in Egypt. The Egyptians treated the Israelites as their slaves and the Pharaoh ordered for all baby boys born amongst the Israelites to be killed.

- Prophet Musa's mother placed him in a basket and let him go in the River Nile to save him. The basket ended up near the Pharaoh's palace and the Pharaoh's wife, Lady Aasia decided to keep the baby.

- When Prophet Musa عليه السلام was a young man he went out of the palace to see the city. He found two people fighting; an Egyptian and an Israelite. He punched the Egyptian to try and stop the fight but the man died.

- Prophet Musa عليه السلام left Egypt and went to Madyan where he helped two women fetch water from a well. Their father, Prophet Shoaib عليه السلام asked him to stay and work in his garden for eight or ten years. After this time he married one of Prophet Shoaib's daughters and returned to Egypt.

- Along the way he saw a tree which appeared to be on fire. A voice came from the tree telling him that he was chosen by Allah ﷻ as a prophet and that he had to go and rescue the Israelites from the Pharaoh.

- He was given two miracles to show the Pharaoh. When he placed his hand under his arm it would shine very bright and when he threw his staff on the floor it would turn into a serpent.

- The Pharaoh refused to believe Prophet Musa عليه السلام so Prophet Musa عليه السلام led the Children of Israel out of Egypt by parting the sea with his staff. The Pharaoh tried to follow with his army but the sea closed and they drowned.

Lessons

- Allah ﷻ saves whoever He wills; the Pharaoh tried his best to kill the prophesised baby but Allah Almighty had Prophet Musa عليه السلام, raised inside the Pharaoh's very own palace. It is said that Prophet Musa عليه السلام used to pull the Pharaoh's beard when he was a baby and the Pharaoh would scream that the baby was out to get him but his wife would assure him that the baby was an innocent child! [Tafsir Ruh al-Bayan]

- Allah dislikes arrogance and destroys anyone who persists in it. Prophet Muhammad ﷺ said that Allah Almighty says, "Pride is My cloak and greatness is My robe; whoever competes with Me in respect to either of them, I shall cast into the Hellfire." [Abu Dawood, Ibn Majah, Ahmad]

- Allah ﷻ always gives a chance to wrongdoers to repent, that is why Prophet Musa عليه السلام was sent to Pharaoh. Allah ﷻ states in the Blessed Qur'an that He does not punish a people until He has sent a messenger to warn them. Prophet Muhammad ﷺ was sent to warn us so we should heed that warning by obeying him and following his teachings.

- In Surah Yunus, ayah number ninety, Allah ﷻ states that when the Pharaoh was drowning and he realised he would not survive, he called out that he believed in God but his faith was rejected because it was insincere - he knew it was the end. Never delay in repentance and in doing a good deed, because it could be the last thing you do. Repentance is accepted right up to the point of death, but the doors of tawbah close for a person when he sees death and knows that there is no turning back.

- Keep your promises - Prophet Musa عليه السلام kept his promise with Prophet Shoaib عليه السلام and worked for him for the agreed time.

Prophet Harun

عليه السلام

the brother of Prophet Musa عليه السلام

Prophet Musa's Helper

Very Good Speech

16

Prophet Harun عليه السلام

- Prophet Harun ﷺ was Prophet Musa's elder brother.
- Prophet Musa ﷺ asked Allah ﷻ to make Prophet Harun ﷺ his helper in calling the Pharaoh to the right path because Prophet Harun ﷺ spoke beautifully and eloquently.
- Allah ﷻ granted Prophet Musa's wish and made Prophet Harun ﷺ his deputy. Together, they called people to the worship of Allah Almighty.
- When Prophet Musa ﷺ would go to the mountain to speak to Allah ﷻ, he would leave Prophet Harun ﷺ in charge of the Israelites.

Lessons

- Prophet Harun العَلِيَّهِ helped Prophet Musa العَلِيَّهِ in his duty. Allah Almighty commands us in the Blessed Qur'an, "Help one another in acts of goodness and piety, and do not assist one another in wrong-doing and transgression." [Surah al-Ma`idah: Ayah 2]
- Use your gifts for the purpose of good, like Prophet Harun العَلِيَّهِ used his eloquence to invite people to the right path.
- Prophet Harun العَلِيَّهِ was older than Prophet Musa العَلِيَّهِ but was made his deputy. He did not see this as an insult because he was the elder. When serving the cause of righteousness then one has to overcome feelings of jealousy, pride and such things.
- Be selfless if you are chosen for the path of Allah Almighty.

Prophet Dawood

عليه السلام

زبور

The Psalms
of David

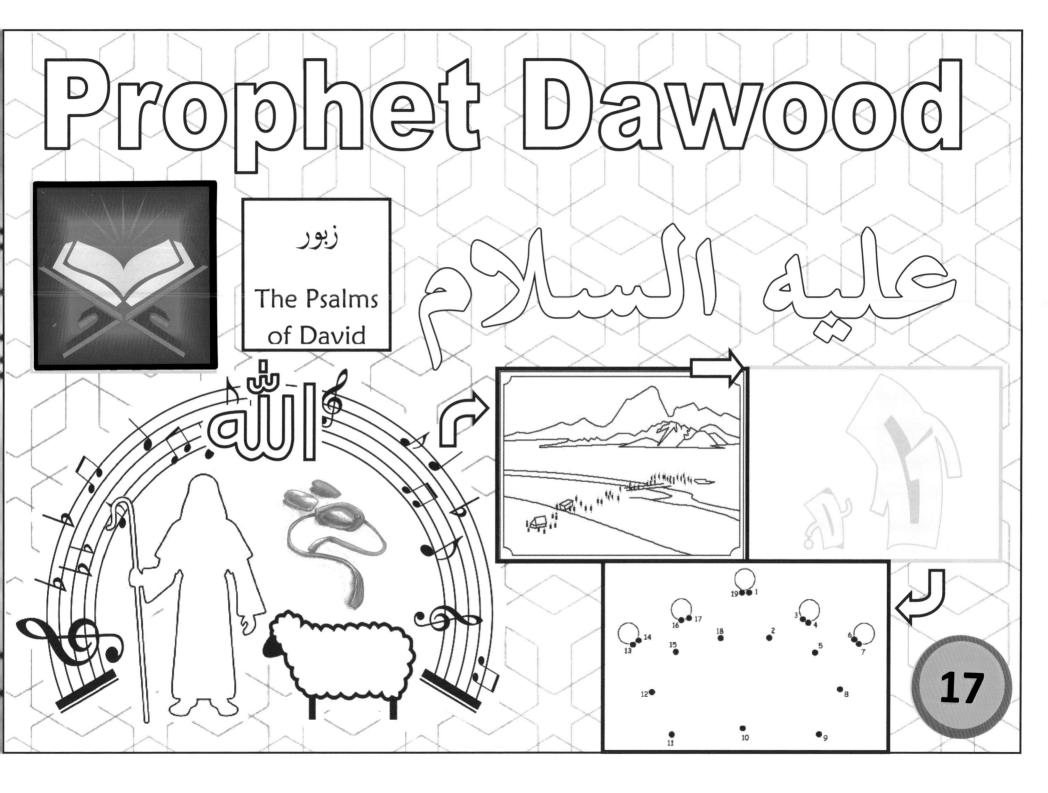

17

Prophet Dawood عليه السلام

- Prophet Dawood عليه السلام was a descendent of Judah, one of the sons of Prophet Ya'qub عليه السلام.
- He is known as the Prophet David in the Bible and Torah.
- Prophet Dawood عليه السلام was a shepherd as a young man and had a beautiful voice with which he would sing the praises of Allah ﷻ. He sang so beautifully that the mountains and birds sang with him.
- The King Talut (King Saul in the Bible) led his army to fight the army of Jalut (Goliath).
- Prophet Dawood عليه السلام was in King Talut's army. Allah ﷻ tested the army by commanding them not to drink from the river they were crossing even though they were hot and tired. Most of the soldiers drank the water and this took away their courage to fight Jalut.
- Prophet Dawood عليه السلام did not drink the water and faced Jalut alone with just his sling and a few pebbles. He killed Jalut and Jalut's army was defeated.
- Prophet Dawood عليه السلام became the king after King Talut died and Allah ﷻ gave him great wisdom. He used his wisdom to unite the twelve tribes of Israel who had become divided.
- Allah ﷻ gave Prophet Dawood عليه السلام the knowledge of making chain-mail armour.
- He was given divine scripture called Zabur (the Psalms).

Lessons

- Prophet Dawood's story teaches us that size, physical strength and number do not make a difference if you have strength of faith and conviction. Prophet Dawood عليه السلام was a youth when he defeated the grand warrior Jalut with a simple weapon. Allah Almighty states in the Blessed Qur'an when mentioning this story, "How often a small force has defeated a large army with God's permission! God is with those who are steadfast." [Surah Al-Baqarah: Ayah 249]

- It doesn't require much to divide people; assumption, spying and tale-telling are enough to do that. True wisdom is bringing together divided people, like Prophet Dawood عليه السلام did with the twelve tribes of Israel.

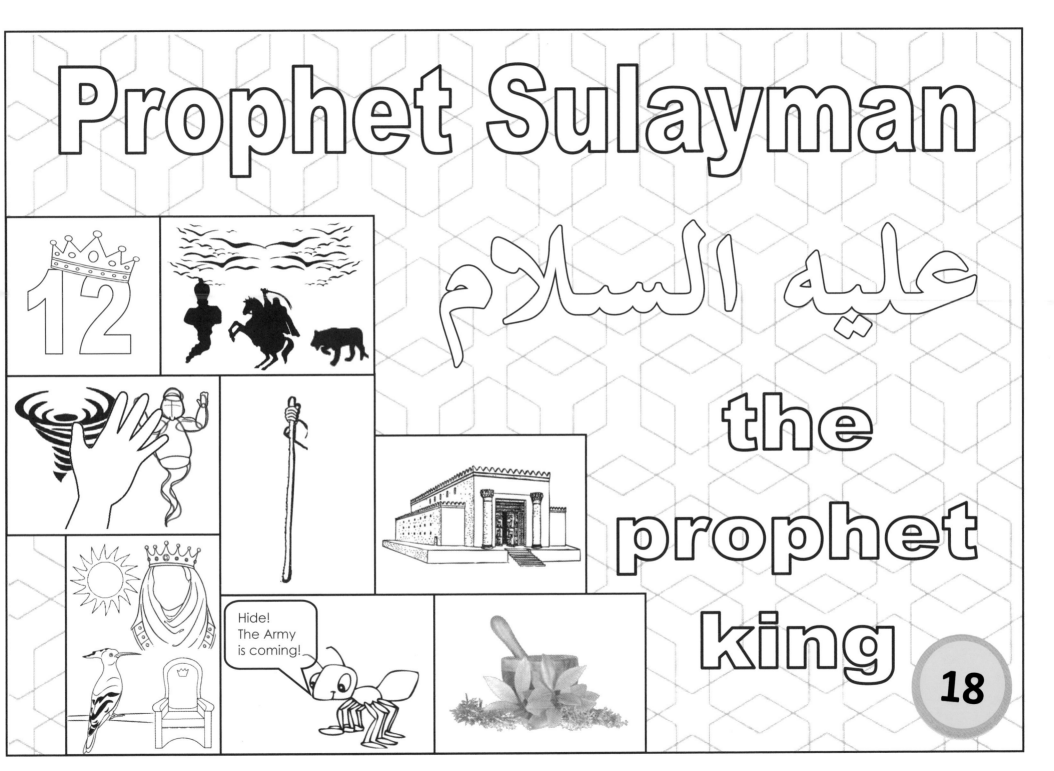

Prophet Sulayman عليه السلام

- Prophet Sulayman ﷺ was the son of Prophet Dawood ﷺ.
- He is known as Prophet Solomon in the Bible and Torah.
- He became King of the Israelites when he was just twelve years old and he had a great kingdom.
- He was given power to control the wind and he had control over the jinn, who worked for him and built great buildings. It is said that Prophet Sulayman ﷺ rebuilt Masjid Al-Aqsa.
- His army included humans, jinn, animals and birds.
- He understood the languages of animals and birds.
- A hoopoe bird (hudhud) once told him of a queen whose people worshipped the sun. She was Bilqees, the Queen of Sheba and she had a great throne. Prophet Sulayman ﷺ wrote her a letter inviting her to worship Allah. She came to visit Prophet Sulayman ﷺ and became a Muslim.
- Once when Prophet Sulayman ﷺ was travelling with his army, he was amused to hear an ant miles away telling her fellow ants to hide in their anthill because the army of Sulayman ﷺ was coming and they might trample over the ants without realising. He smiled when he heard this.
- Prophet Sulayman ﷺ was given the knowledge of medicinal plants and their healing powers.
- When he passed away he was leaning on his staff overseeing the jinn workers. They did not realise he had passed away for a long time. It was only when termites ate through his staff that the jinn realised that Prophet Sulayman ﷺ had passed away.

Lessons

- Animals have languages which can be understood by those chosen by Allah ﷻ.

- The huge throne of Queen Bilqees was transported hundreds of miles in the blink of an eye by one of Prophet Sulayman's companions (known as Asif bin Barkhiyaa). He was able to do this because he possessed some knowledge of Divine scripture. This incident, which is mentioned in Surah an-Naml, shows that Allah Almighty gives the ability to bend the laws of physics to anyone He chooses. Miracles are true and Allah ﷻ shows us His signs through Prophets as well as pious people; but being steadfast and staying on the right path is better than any miracle.

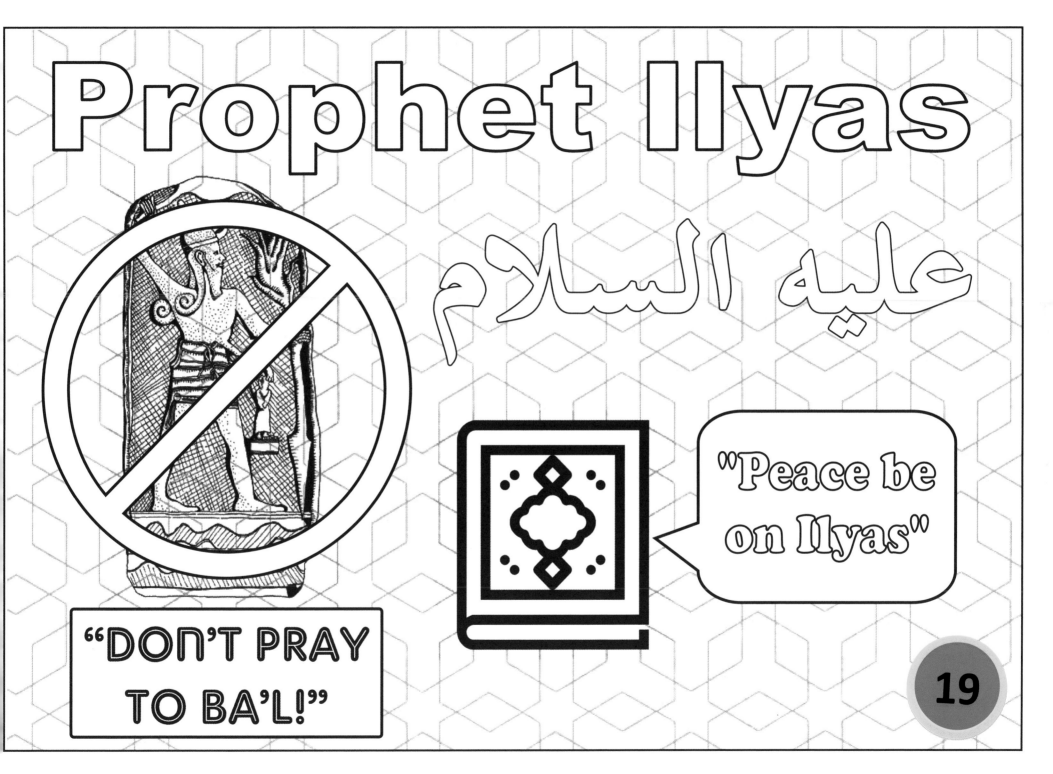

Prophet Ilyas عليه السلام

- Prophet Ilyas عليه السلام was a descendent of Prophet Harun عليه السلام.
- It is said that he is known in the Jewish and Christian tradition as Elias or Elijah.
- His people turned to idol worship. They believed in many gods including the chief god who they called Ba'l. Prophet Ilyas عليه السلام told them not to pray to Ba'l, but to worship Allah Almighty.
- Allah Almighty rewarded Prophet Ilyas عليه السلام by mentioning the words, 'peace be on Ilyas,' in the Blessed Qur'an. Now everyone who recites the Qur'an will send greetings of peace upon him until the Day of Judgement.

Lessons

- Idol worship is the worst sin, all prophets warned against it. In ancient Mesopotamia, the word Ba'al meant 'lord' so it was used for many idols worshiped by the polytheists but usually it was used to refer to the chief idol. We tend to think that polytheism means bowing down before a carved sculpture but in fact Allah Almighty warns us in the Blessed Qur'an, "Consider the one who has taken his own desire as a god..." [Surah Al-Jathiya: Ayah 23] Perhaps selfishness, self-centeredness and narcissism (excessive self-love) is the ugly face of polytheism in our age.

Prophet Alyasa' عليه السلام

- Prophet Alyasa' عليه السلام was a descendent of Prophet Ilyas عليه السلام, who was a descendent of Prophet Harun عليه السلام, who was a descendent of Levi who was the son of Prophet Ya'qub عليه السلام who was the son of Prophet Ishaq عليه السلام who was the son of Prophet Ibrahim *Khalilullah* عليه السلام.
- He was sent to guide the Children of Israel.
- He is described in the Blessed Qur'an very briefly. It states that he is amongst the chosen ones who Allah ﷻ guided along the straight path, and amongst those whom Allah ﷻ favoured in the worlds.
- It is said that he is known to the Jews and Christians as Prophet Elisha.

Lessons

- Prophet Alyasa' was amongst the chosen people on the straight path and the favoured ones. We ask Allah ﷻ in every salah to guide us along the straight path; the path of those whom Allah ﷻ favoured. The favoured ones are: *al-nabiyyin* (the prophets), *al-siddiqin* (the true ones), *al-shuhada* (the martyrs) and *al-salihin* (the righteous ones). Allah almighty chose around 124,000 people to be amongst the prophets and they all came to guide humanity at their appointed time in the world and the door of prophethood is now closed and sealed. We can try and have our names written amongst the other three categories by doing good deeds and living a life of piety and goodness and asking Allah ﷻ to include us with the chosen ones or at least grant us their love and their company.

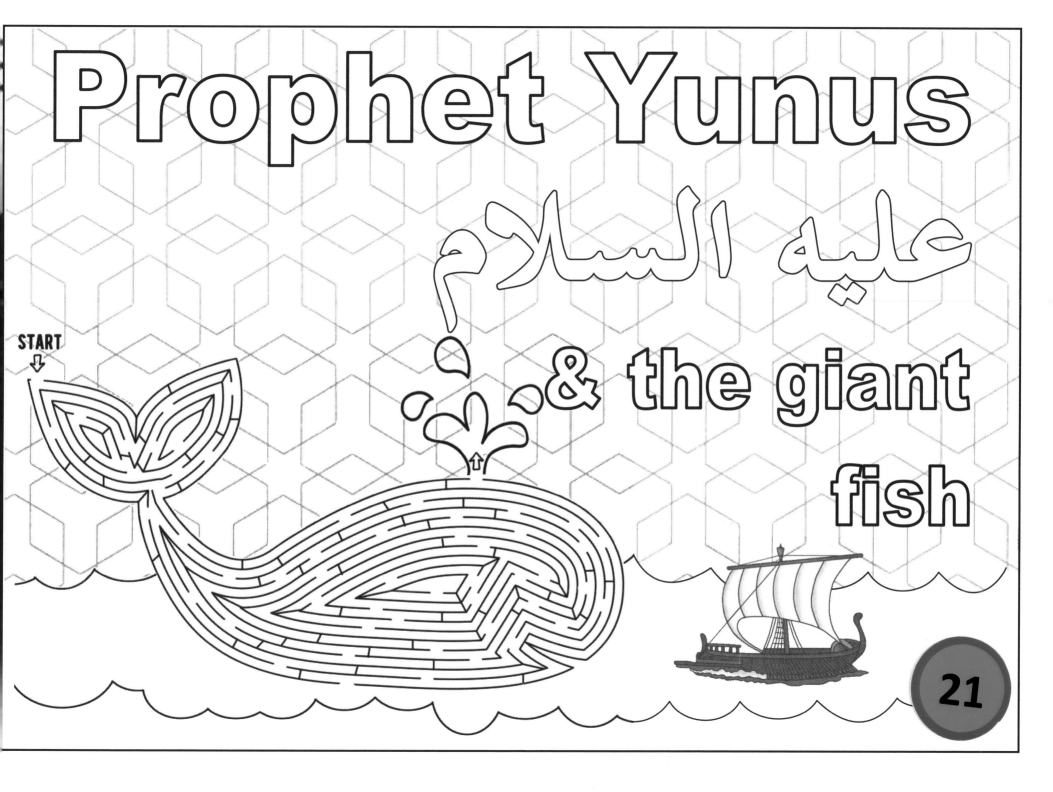

Prophet Yunus عليه السلام

- Prophet Yunus عليه السلام was a descendent of Prophet Sulayman عليه السلام.
- In the Bible he is called Prophet Jonah.
- As well as being called by his name 'Yunus' in the Blessed Qur'an he is also called 'Dhun-Nun' which means 'the one with the fish.' This refers to an incident when he was swallowed by a giant fish.
- He was told by Allah ﷻ to go to the city of Ninevah and call the people to the straight path.
- The people of Ninevah did not listen to his message. He warned them of Allah Almighty's punishment and left in anger at them. The people were afraid and repented to Allah ﷻ, asking for forgiveness, so the punishment did not come.
- Prophet Yunus عليه السلام, meanwhile, boarded a ship. When the ship set sail, it became stuck at sea and the people on board decided that the ship was overloaded and someone had to be thrown overboard. They drew lots and the name of Prophet Yunus عليه السلام came up so he had to jump overboard and he was swallowed by a giant fish.
- From the belly of the fish he called out to Allah ﷻ for help. The fish threw him out onto the shore where he lay in a very ill state unable to move. Allah ﷻ caused a tree to grow beside him which sheltered him and Allah ﷻ cared for him until he was better and then told him to return to Ninevah and teach the people about Allah Almighty.

Lessons

- Storming off in anger at a situation is not usually a good way to resolve the situation; especially for someone who is in charge. Being the head or leader requires a lot of patience.
- The punishment of Allah ﷻ can be averted by repenting sincerely to Him.

Prophet Zakariyya

عليه السلام

the father of
Prophet Yahya

the guardian of
Lady Maryam

...your sign shall be
that you will not speak
to anyone for three days...

22

Prophet Zakariyya عليه السلام

- Prophet Zakariyya عليه السلام is known as Prophet Zachariah in the Jewish and Christian scriptures.
- He was the guardian of Prophet Isa's mother - Lady Maryam. When Lady Maryam was just a child, she was taken by her mother, Hannah, to the temple in Jerusalem to serve God there. Prophet Zakariyya عليه السلام was chosen as her guardian after drawing lots.
- Whenever he visited Lady Maryam in her sanctuary to see if she needed anything, he would find that she had food already - fresh fruit which was not even in season - so he asked her where the fruit had come from. She said it was from Allah عز وجل.
- Prophet Zakariyya عليه السلام was an old man but had no children of his own, so when he saw this out of season fruit, he prayed to Allah to grant him a child, even though him and his wife were past the normal age for having children.
- Allah Almighty accepted his prayer and sent angels with the good news of a son who would be called Prophet Yahya عليه السلام. Prophet Zakariyya عليه السلام asked Allah عز وجل for a sign of this true news and Allah عز وجل said that you will not speak to anyone for three days, so Prophet Zakariyya عليه السلام gestured to his people to pray to Allah عز وجل.
- It is mentioned in a hadith that Prophet Zakariyya عليه السلام was a carpenter.

Lessons

- Women and men are equal in the sight of God in terms of their purpose in life which is to gain the nearness of Allah ﷻ. Although there may be different roles for them to fulfil in this world and they may take different paths in life by doing different actions, Allah ﷻ rewards everyone's actions based on how sincere their hearts are, not whether they are male or female.

- When Prophet Zakariyya عليه السلام saw the miraculous fruit in Lady Maryam's sanctuary, he supplicated to Allah ﷻ there and then in the sanctuary because he saw the Lady Maryam was a chosen servant of Allah Almighty and the places where such people stay and worship Allah ﷻ are filled with Allah Almighty's blessings. His supplication was accepted and Prophet Yahya عليه السلام was born.

Prophet Yahya

عليه السلام

His name will be Yahya.
We have given that name
to none before him.

Fruit, leaves & grass

have courage and be kind

23

Prophet Yahya عليه السلام

- Prophet Yahya الَعَلَيْهِ was the son of Prophet Zakariyya الَعَلَيْهِ.
- He was born miraculously to Prophet Zakariyya الَعَلَيْهِ and his wife Ishba' (Elizabeth) when they were very old.
- No one was given this name before him.
- He is known amongst the Jewish and Christian communities as John the Baptist.
- He was given knowledge and wisdom even as a young child - some people said when he was only two or three years old. He was told to hold tightly to the [teachings of the] Book of Allah ﷻ.
- Allah ﷻ made Prophet Yahya الَعَلَيْهِ very kind and compassionate towards others. The Blessed Qur'an mentions especially that he was kind to his parents and never ever disrespected or disobeyed them.
- He would eat fruit, leaves and grass to live a simple life and he cried so much out of love for Allah ﷻ that his tears left ridge marks on his cheeks.
- The Blessed Qur'an says about Prophet Yahya الَعَلَيْهِ: "So peace be on him the day he was born, the day he died, and the day he will be brought back to life."

Lessons

- Like Prophet Yahya ﷺ, we should be kind and compassionate towards others. We should have empathy for anyone who is distressed and do what we can to help. Allah ﷻ loves those who help his creatures.

- We should be especially kind to our parents, and even more so if they are in old age. It is a major sin to disobey your parents. We should try to do chores and errands for them without complaining and with a smile if possible. We should try to attend to their needs and think of how to serve them so that they don't have to ask anyone else. If they become ill we should be more caring and be sensitive so they always feel dignified. If we have lost one or both of our parents we should pray for them with each salah and also continue to keep links with their friends on their behalf.

- We also learn the lesson of simple living from the story of Prophet Yahya ﷺ, especially regarding food. Don't get too indulgent with a lavish lifestyle because everything in this world is temporary. We should think about the grave and the next life and try to follow in the footsteps of Prophet Yahya ﷺ and our beloved Prophet Muhammad ﷺ who would cry out of love for Allah ﷻ and out of fear of displeasing Him.

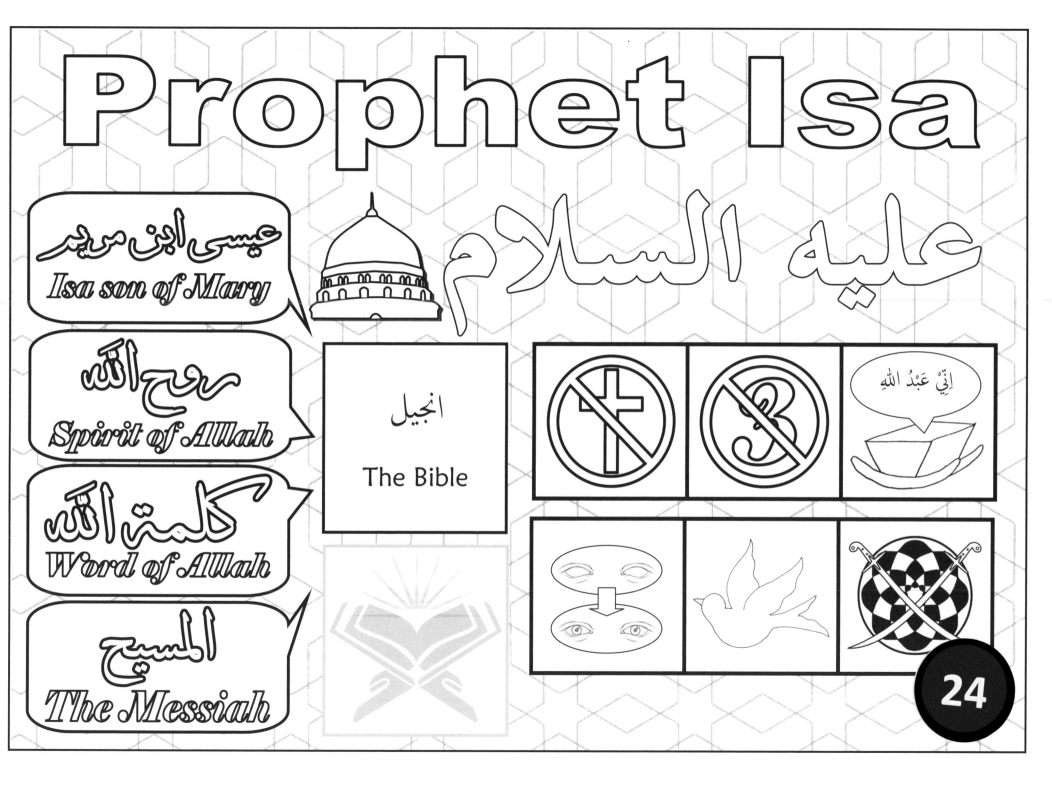

Prophet Isa عليه السلام

- Prophet Isa السلام is known as Prophet Jesus in the Bible, the holy book he was given.
- He was the miracle baby of Lady Maryam (Mary), and he had no father.
- He spoke in his crib when he was a new-born baby to defend his mother and tell the people that he was the slave of Allah ﷻ (not the son of God) and a prophet who had been given divine scripture.
- He was given miracles by Allah ﷻ that he could cure blind people and heal sick people. He could make bird shapes out of clay which would become real live birds when he blew into them. He knew what people had eaten and what they had left stored in their homes. He could also bring the dead to life.
- He did not preach belief in the trinity but called people towards the worship of One God.
- The Christians believed he was crucified and died on the cross but the Blessed Qur'an states very clearly that he was not killed nor crucified, it was made to appear this way and in fact, he was raised to Heaven by Allah Almighty.
- He has been given the following names and titles in the Blessed Qur'an: Isa ibn Maryam - Jesus, son of Mary; Roohullah - The Spirit of Allah (meaning his spirit was chosen by Allah ﷻ to be special); Kalimatullah - The Word of Allah; Al-Maseeh - The Messiah
- He will return to Earth to fight the forces of Dajjal and defeat them. He will rule the Earth as a just and fair ruler. When he dies he will be buried in Madinah al-Munawwarah next to Prophet Muhammad ﷺ (under the green dome).

Lessons

- According to Allah Almighty's law, every child has a mother and a father, except when Allah wills. He created Prophet Adam العليه السلام without a mother and father and he created Prophet Isa العليه السلام without a father. We learn from this that Allah عزّوجلّ is the Creator of the natural laws which govern the world but is not bound by them.
- Prophet Isa العليه السلام did not have a father, however this does NOT make him the son of God.
- During his time the knowledge of medicine was regarded as the cutting edge of scientific research so he was given miracles by Allah Almighty which would baffle the most skilled physicians and doctors. He could cure the incurable, he could cure death itself!

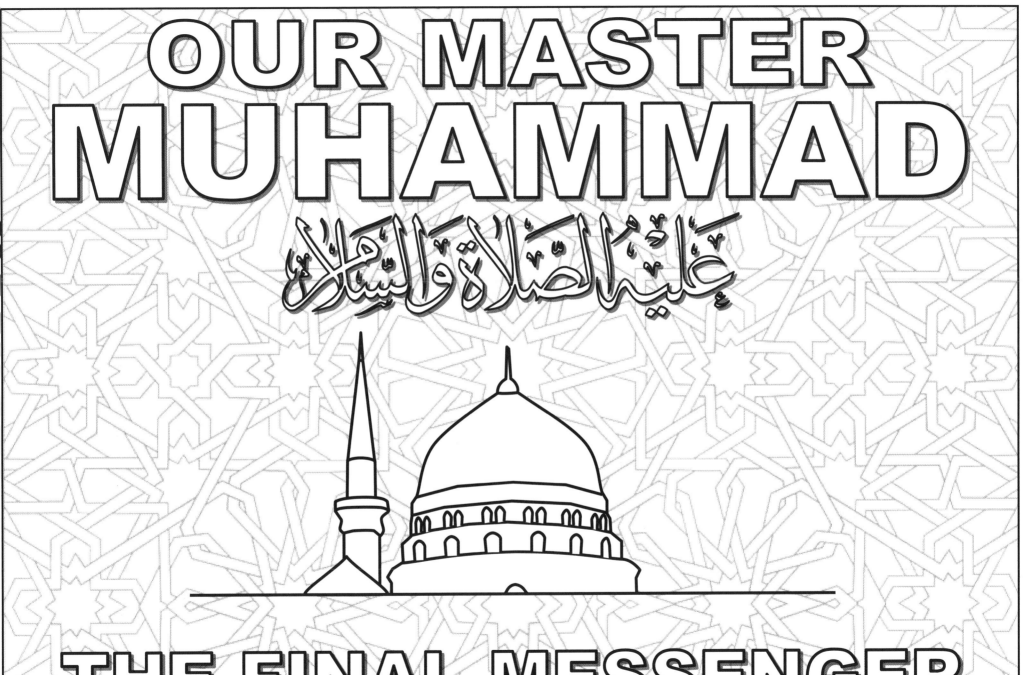

Our Master, Prophet Muhammad عليه الصلاة و السلام

- Prophet Muhammad ﷺ is the final Messenger of Allah; no prophets or messengers will come after him.
- He was born in the city of Makkah al-Mukarramah in the year 620 CE
- He lived a pure and noble life and was recognised as "As-Saadiq" (the truthful one) and "Al-Ameen" (the trustworthy one) from his youth onwards.
- At the age of twenty-five he married the noble Lady Khadija ﷺ and they started a family.
- He was given revelation in the form of the Blessed Qur'an at the age of forty, while he was in the cave of Hira worshipping Allah ﷻ during the month of Ramadan.
- He called the people of Makkah to leave idol worship and believe in One God. They rejected his message and drove him and his followers out of their city.
- The Prophet ﷺ migrated to Madinah al-Munawwarah in the north and began to spread the word of Allah ﷻ from there.
- The people of Makkah continued to attack the Muslims even in Madinah but the Prophet ﷺ wanted peace so he made a peace treaty with them by accepting all their conditions.
- The people of Makkah broke the agreement so the Prophet ﷺ took control of the city of Makkah and restored the peace. He forgave all the people who had hurt him and driven him from his home.
- The Prophet ﷺ passed away in Madinah al-Munawwarah at the age of sixty-three and is buried under the green dome in the south-eastern corner of al-Masjid an-Nabawiyy (The Prophet's Mosque).

Lessons

- Prophet Muhammad ﷺ is the perfect example, sent with perfect and complete guidance, i.e. the Noble Quran. We should study his life in detail and adopt his characteristics. Here is a glimpse of them:
- Being truthful and trustworthy are two qualities which form the basis of good character.
- The basis for a marriage proposal should be a good Deen and good manners which is what Lady Khadija ﷺ saw in Prophet Muhammad ﷺ when she proposed to him.
- Giving way for peace: When the people of Makkah al-Mukarramah stopped the Muslims from entering the city for the pilgrimage of the Holy Ka'ba, they sent a very clever man to negotiate a peace treaty on their behalf. The terms they proposed were heavily biased, they took the upper hand on every point of discussion. To the dismay of many companions, the Noble Prophet ﷺ accepted all their terms and gave way in everything just so that there could be peace for at least ten years. Some of the companions felt humiliated by the treaty but Allah ﷺ called it a clear victory in the Blessed Qur'an because it paved the way for communication and ultimately for people to see the beauty of Islam and enter into it in the droves. The Prophet ﷺ was a messenger of mercy not a man of war and conquest.
- Forgiveness: Although the people of Makkah al-Mukarramah boycotted, persecuted, tortured and murdered the Muslims for simply believing in one God; when the Prophet ﷺ returned to the city as a victor a decade later, he did not order revenge killings or any retaliation of the sort. He offered sanctuary, protection and forgiveness for anyone who sought it. He was humble entering the city with his head bowed and thanked Allah ﷺ for such a victory. A remarkable example in history.

IRAM: THE CITY OF COLUMNS